Secrets

Wise Publications
London / New York / Sydney / Paris / Copenhagen / Madrid

*This publication is not authorised for sale in
the United States of America and /or Canada*

Exclusive Distributors:
Music Sales Limited
8/9 Frith Street, London W1V 5TZ, England.
Music Sales Pty Limited
120 Rothschild Avenue Rosebery, NSW 2018,
Australia.

Order No.AM942997
ISBN 0-7119-6423-8

This book © Copyright 1997
by Wise Publications
Visit the Internet Music Shop at
http://www.musicsales.co.uk

Unauthorised reproduction of any
part of this publication by any means including
photocopying is an infringement of copyright.

With the exception of 'Un-Break My Heart':
Music arranged by Roger Day.
Music processed by Paul Ewers Music Design.

Printed in the United Kingdom by
Commercial Colour Press, Forest Gate, London.

Your Guarantee of Quality:
As publishers, we strive to produce
every book to the highest commercial standards.
Whilst endeavouring to retain the original
running order of the recorded album, the book
has been carefully designed to minimise
awkward page turns and to make playing from
it a real pleasure.
Particular care has been given to
specifying acid-free, neutral-sized paper made
from pulps which have not been elemental
chlorine bleached.
This pulp is from farmed sustainable
forests and was produced with special regard
for the environment.
Throughout, the printing and binding have been
planned to ensure a sturdy, attractive publication
which should give years of enjoyment.
If your copy fails to meet our high standards,
please inform us and we will gladly replace it.

Music Sales' complete catalogue
describes thousands of titles and is available in
full colour sections by subject, direct from
Music Sales Limited. Please state your areas
of interest and send a cheque/postal order
for £1.50 for postage to: Music Sales Limited,
Newmarket Road, Bury St. Edmunds, Suffolk
IP33 3YB.

Come On Over Here

Music by Tony Rich. Words by Tony Rich, Marc Nelson & Darrell Spencer

1. Where do you go— when you need good lov-in', and how will you know.
(Verse 2 see block lyric)

© Copyright 1996 Otna Oundsa Music/Stiff Shirt Music Incorporated,
Personal 21 Publishing, Bush Burnin' Music Incorporated & Stepping Into The Blue Publishing, USA.
Warner Chappell Music Publishing, 129 Park Street, London W1 (25%)/
MCA Music Limited, 77 Fulham Palace Road, London W6 (25%)/Copyright Control (50%).
All Rights Reserved. International Copyright Secured.

Verse 2:
What do you do
When you're not satisfied?
And when you've done all that you can.
You know you tried, oh yeah.
And how do you say that
You need to get away?
Don't make it so hard
When I'm there for you.

You're Makin Me High

Words & Music by Bryce Wilson & Babyface

© Copyright 1996 ECAF Music/Sony/ATV Songs LLC & 1996 Groove 79 Music/Almo Music Corporation, USA.
Rondor Music (London) Limited, 10A Parsons Green, London SW6 (50%)/
Sony/ATV Music Publishing, 10 Great Marlborough Street, London W1 (50%).
All Rights Reserved. International Copyright Secured.

that's why I want you so bad,_____ just one night of moon - light with

you here in - side__ me. All_____ night, do-in' it a - gain__ and a - gain,__

you know I want you so bad,_____ ba - by, ba - by, ba - by,

CHORUS

ba - by, ba - by, ba - by, ba - by. Ooh, I get so high,__ when I'm a - round you ba - by

I can touch the sky — you make my tem-pera-ture rise. — Ooh
(rise. _____)

ba - by you're mak - in' me high, — ba - by, ba - by, ba - by, ba - by.

I want to feel your heart and soul in - side of me. Let's make a deal, you

roll, I lick and we can go fly - ing in - to ec - sta - sy. Oh dar - lin' you and me,

light my fire, blow my flame, take me, take me, take me, a - way.

All I real - ly want is

D.%. repeat chorus to fade

Verse 2:
Can't get my mind off you,
I think I might be obsessed.
The very thought of you
Makes me want to get undressed.
I wanna be with you
In spite of what my heart says,
I guess I want you too bad,
All I want is
Moonlight, with you there inside me
All night, doin' it again and again,
You know I want you so bad,
Baby, baby, baby, baby.

There's No Me Without You

Words & Music by Babyface

© Copyright 1996 ECAF Music & Sony/ATV Songs LLC, USA.
Sony/ATV Music Publishing, 10 Great Marlborough Street, London W1.
All Rights Reserved. International Copyright Secured.

moon with-out____ you, there's no Sat-ur-day nights____ with-out____

____ you, there's no walk through the park,____ no beat in my heart,____ no I

To Coda ⊕ **1.**

love you, no I can't live with-out____ you. You

told me ev-'ry-thing would be cool,____ said I would-n't al - ways feel blue.____

Un-Break My Heart

Words & Music by Diane Warren

© Copyright 1996 Realsongs, USA.
EMI Songs Limited, 127 Charing Cross Road, London WC2.
All Rights Reserved. International Copyright Secured.

you caused when you walked out the door and walked out of my life. Un - cry these tears

To Coda

I cried so man - y nights. Un - break my heart.

DON'T CRY FOR ME ARGENTINA

It won't be easy, you'll think it strange When I try to explain how I
feel That I still need your love after all that I've done
You won't believe me All you will see is a girl you once knew
Although she's dressed up to the nines At sixes and sevens with you
I had to let it happen, I had to change Couldn't stay all my life
down at heel Looking out of the window, staying out of the sun
So I chose freedom Running around trying everything new
But nothing impressed me at all I never expected it to

Don't cry for me Argentina The truth is I never left you
All through my wild days My mad existence
I kept my promise Don't keep your distance

And as for fortune, and as for fame I never invited them in
Though it seemed to the world they were all I desired
They are illusions They are not the solutions they promised to be
The answer was here all the time I love you and hope you love me
Don't cry for me Argentina...

Don't cry for me Argentina The truth is I never left you
All through my wild days My mad existence I kept my promise
Don't keep your distance

Have I said too much? There's nothing more I can think of to say to
you
But all you have to do is look at me to know that every word is true

THE SHOOP SHOOP SONG

Does he love me I want to know How can I tell if he loves me so
Is it in his eyes? Oh no! You'll be deceived
Is it in his sighs? Oh no! He'll make believe
If you want to know if he loves you so It's in his kiss
That's where it is

Is it in his face? Oh no! That's just his charms
In his warm embrace? Oh no! That's just his arms
If you want to know if he loves you so It's in his kiss
That's where it is It's in his kiss
That's where it is

Kiss him and squeeze him tight Find out what you want to know
If it's love, if it really is It's there in his kiss

How about the way he acts Oh no! That's not the way
And you're not list'nin' to all I say If you wanna know if he loves
you so It's in his kiss That's where it is
It's in his kiss That's where it is

Kiss him and squeeze him tight Find out what you want to know
If it's love, if it really ismIt's there in his kiss
How about the way he acts Oh no! That's not the way
And you're not list'nin' to all I say If you wanna know if he loves
you so It's in his kiss That's where it is
It's in his kiss That's where it is

Talking In His Sleep

Music by Keith Crouch
Words by Toni Braxton

Spoken: So you know ev'rything about your lover? Wanna bet? 1. My oh— my,— how can this— be,— there he— goes,— talk-ing in his sleep. By and— by— he will con - nive,— does he— know— he's talk-ing in his sleep?

To Coda ⊕

© Copyright 1996 Lady Ashlee Incorporated/Jay Bird Alley Music Incorporated & Human Rhythm Music, USA.
EMI Music Publishing Limited, 127 Charing Cross Road, London WC2 (50%)/Copyright Control (50%).
All Rights Reserved. International Copyright Secured.

Verse 2: (spoken)
Adultery,
That's what they call it
When you're married.
Tell me something,
Why is it that the men are forgiven and the women aren't?
I don't know, maybe,
Maybe I should forgive him,
Maybe I'm overreacting, what do you think?

(sung)
The promises he made,
Said we'd be together for always.
He's such a liar,
Then he calls out her name.

Verse 3:(spoken)
Guilty secrets...
They are haunting my life...
And he doesn't even know that I know...
Can you hear him?...

(sung)
The promises he made,
Said we'd be together for always.
He's such a liar,
Then he goes out to burn me.

How Could An Angel Break My Heart

Words & Music by Babyface & Toni Braxton

© Copyright 1996 ECAF Music & Sony/ATV Songs LLC & Lady Ashlee Incorporated/Jay Bird Alley Music Incorporated, USA.
Sony/ATV Music Publishing, 10 Great Marlborough Street, London W1 (90%)/Copyright Control (10%).
All Rights Reserved. International Copyright Secured.

be-cause that lul - la - by was mine._____   I heard he sealed it with a

kiss,   he gent - ly kissed her cher - ry

lips,_____   I found that so hard to be -

lieve,_____   be - cause his kiss be - longed to

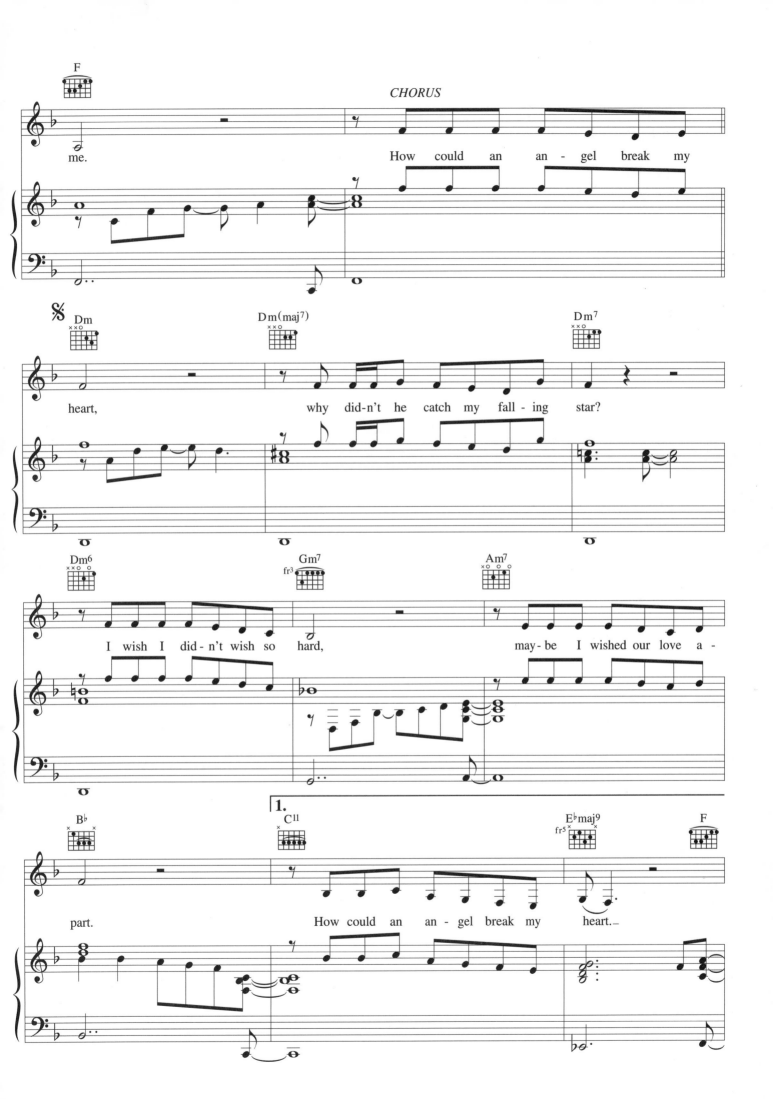

CHORUS

me.

How could an an-gel break my

heart,   why did-n't he catch my fall-ing star?

I wish I did - n't wish so   hard,   may - be I wished our love a -

1.

part.   How could an an-gel break my heart.—

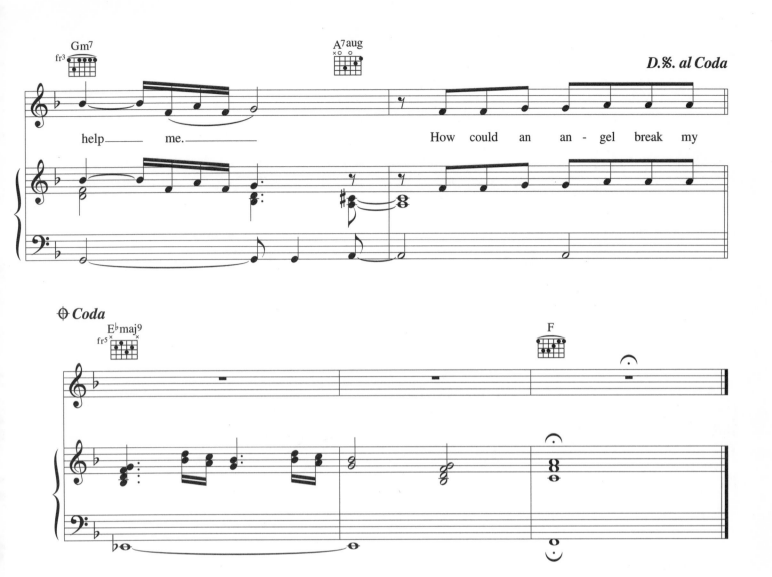

Verse 2:
I heard her face was white as rain,
Soft as a rose that blooms in May,
He keeps her picture in a frame,
And when he sleeps he calls her name.
I wonder if she makes him smile
The way he used to smile at me,
I hope she doesn't make him laugh,
Because his laugh belongs to me.

Find Me A Man

Words & Music by Babyface

© Copyright 1996 ECAF Music & Sony/ATV Songs LLC, USA.
Sony/ATV Music Publishing, 10 Great Marlborough Street, London W1.
All Rights Reserved. International Copyright Secured.

Verse 2:
I'm just a girl
That likes a man that knows his right from wrong,
One that will keep his loving at home.
I'm the kind of girl
Who likes to please her man the whole night long, ooh,
But he's gotta please me just as long.

Why Should I Care

Words & Music by Babyface

1. Back in the day___ when I was young - er, I
(Verse 2 see block lyric)

was - n't a - fraid___ of giv - ing my heart___ to___ you.___

© Copyright 1996 ECAF Music & Sony/ATV Songs LLC, USA.
Sony/ATV Music Publishing, 10 Great Marlborough Street, London W1.
All Rights Reserved. International Copyright Secured.

Verse 2:
Back in the day I shoulda been wiser,
But what can I say, I shoulda been onto you.
But I was afraid that you'd break my heart in two,
Fate would have it that you broke it anyway baby.
And every time I close my eyes, I just remind myself,
You told about a million lies, you put my heart through hell.
And now you wanna get with me, just for old times' sake,
Well I am not about to make that same mistake.

Let It Flow

Words & Music by Babyface

1. First thing___ Mon - day morn ___ - ing, I'm gon - na pack my tears a -
(Verse 2 see block lyric)

way.

Got no cause to look back___

© Copyright 1996 ECAF Music & Sony/ATV Songs LLC & Fox Film Music Corporation, USA.
Sony/ATV Music Publishing, 10 Great Marlborough Street, London W1 (87.5%) & Fox Music Publishing/
EMI Music Publishing Limited, 127 Charing Cross Road, London WC2 (12.5%).
All Rights Reserved. International Copyright Secured.

Verse 2:

Don't nobody want no broke heart
And don't nobody want no two time losers,
Ain't nobody gonna love you like you are
If you take whatever he brings your way,
You see the thing of it,
Is we deserve respect,
But we can't command respect without change.
There comes a time when we must go our own way.

I Don't Want To

Words & Music by R. Kelly

© Copyright 1996 Kelly Publishing Incorporated/Zomba Songs Incorporated, USA.
Zomba Music Publishers Limited, 165-167 High Road, Willesden, London NW10.
All Rights Reserved. International Copyright Secured.

Verse 2:
I really don't feel like smiling anymore,
And I haven't had the peace to sleep at all.
Ever since you went away, baby my whole life has changed,
I don't want to love and I don't want to live.

In The Late Of Night

Words & Music by Babyface & Jonathan Buck

Al - ways thought your pro - mise was for life, I did not think that I would hear you say good - bye._____ And I al - ways heard you led an - oth - er life, I doubt - ed ev - 'ry

© Copyright 1996 Vibe Zelect Music/Yab Yum Music, ECAF Music & Sony/ATV Songs LLC, USA.
Sony/ATV Music Publishing, 10 Great Marlborough Street, London W1.
All Rights Reserved. International Copyright Secured.

2°
In my eyes
You will always be the lucky one,
'Cause you know you'll always have my love
For all times until I die.
Through the end I gave to you my best,
You gave, you gave me loneliness.

I Love Me Some Him

Music by SoulShock & Karlin
Words by SoulShock, Karlin, Andrea Martin & Gloria Stewart

© Copyright 1996 EMI-Casadida Music Publishing & EMI Music Publishing (Sweden),
Sailandra/Almo Music Corporation & Plaything/Too True Songs, USA.
EMI Music Publishing Limited, 127 Charing Cross Road, London WC2 (50%)/
Warner Chappell Music Limited, 129 Park Street, London W1 (25%)/Copyright Control (25%).
All Rights Reserved. International Copyright Secured.

Verse 2:
Just like a dream come true,
I wished for you.
I have never been so happy
'Bout a love so new.
You opened my heart to a brand new start
My love's there wherever you are,
I won't let no one
Take you away.

10/97 (29211)